ALFRED's
SACRED PERFORMER
COLLECTIONS

ADVANCED PIANO

Inspirational Christmas Medleys

9 Solo Piano Arrangements of Timeless Carols

nged by **Mary K. Sallee**

I love the Christmas season because it gives me an opportunity to connect with the past by remembering the wonderful carols I grew up singing and playing at my church. This collection of medleys combines many of my favorite carols, from well-loved standards to carols and lullabies from the rich cultures of several other countries.

The pieces are arranged to combine similar textual themes or moods, and can be used in a variety of settings. I hope these medleys help you connect to your own wonderful Christmas memories, and bring to light some fresh new melodies and sounds from around the world.

Mary K. Sallee

Alfred Music
P.O. Box 10003
Van Nuys, CA 91410-0003
alfred.com

ISBN-10: 0-7390-9169-7
ISBN-13: 978-0-7390-9169-2

Cover Photos
Fir Tree Branches: © shutterstock.com / SeDmi • Angels Are Playing On Instruments On A Lead-Glass Of A Basillica: © shutterstock.com / Robert Jakatics

Joseph Dearest, Joseph Mine
with
Still, Still, Still / Rocking Carol

German, Austrian and Czech folk carols
Arr. Mary K. Sallee

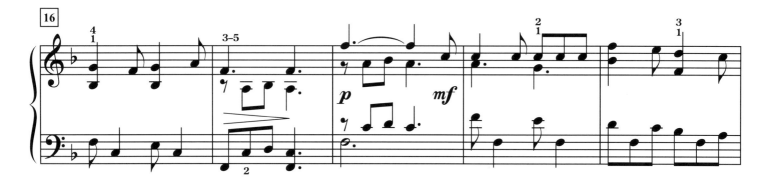

Still, Still, Still

4

O Come, Little Children
with
O Come, All Ye Faithful

Johann Schulz and John F. Wade
Arr. Mary K. Sallee

O Come, All Ye Faithful

Manger Medley
(Cradle Song, Away in a Manger, Lullaby Jesu)

William J. Kirkpatrick, James R. Murray,
and Traditional Polish
Arr. Mary K. Sallee

Away in a Manger

Lullaby Jesu

(Approx. Performance Time – 3:15)

What Child Is This?
with
Coventry Carol / Infant Holy, Infant Lowly

Traditional English and Polish carols
Arr. Mary K. Sallee

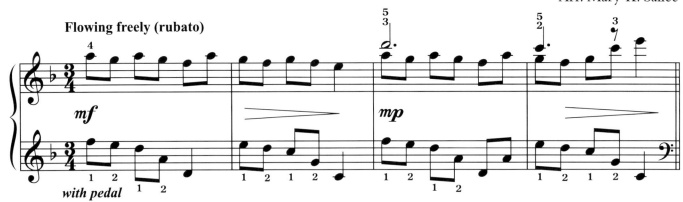

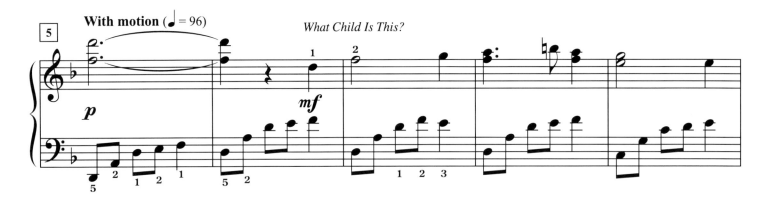

Infant Holy, Infant Lowly

Rise Up, Shepherd, and Follow
with
While Shepherds Watched Their Flocks

Traditional and G. F. Handel
Arr. Mary K. Sallee

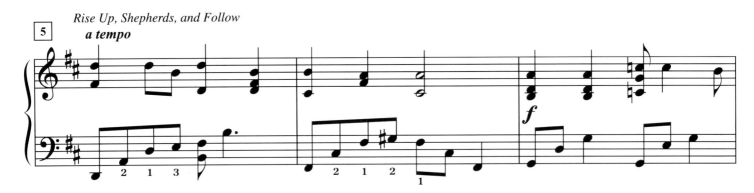

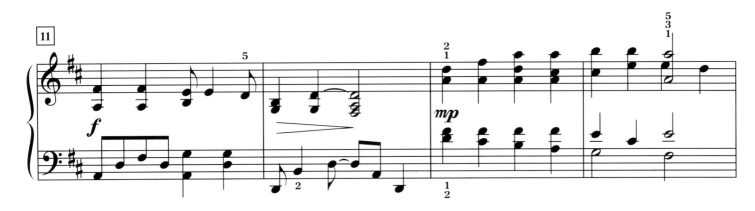

While Shepherds Watched Their Flocks

Personent Hodie
with
We Three Kings

from *Piae Cantiones* and John H. Hopkins, Jr.
Arr. Mary K. Sallee

See Amid the Winter's Snow
with
Lo, How a Rose E'er Blooming

John Goss and Michael Praetorius
Arr. Mary K. Sallee

See Amid the Winter's Snow

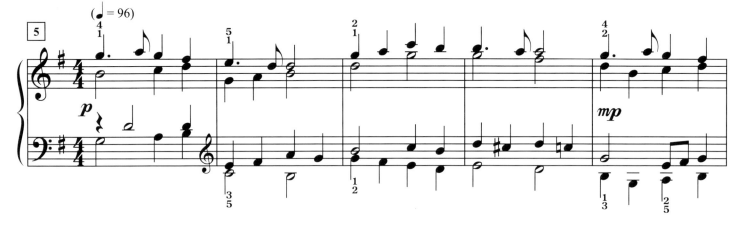

Slowly

(Holly + Ivy)

Lo, How a Rose E'er Blooming

Freely, with movement

Poco più mosso

Tempo I

a tempo

The Holly and the Ivy
with
The Snow Lay on the Ground

Traditional
Arr. Mary K. Sallee

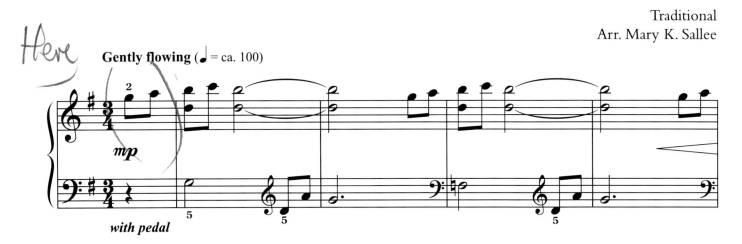

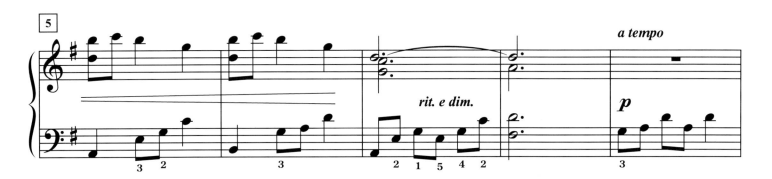

The Snow Lay on the Ground

Brightly (♩. = 100–108)

poco rit. e dim.

To Silent Night

A Silent and Holy Night
(Silent Night *with* O Holy Night)

Franz Grüber and Adolphe Adam
Arr. Mary K. Sallee

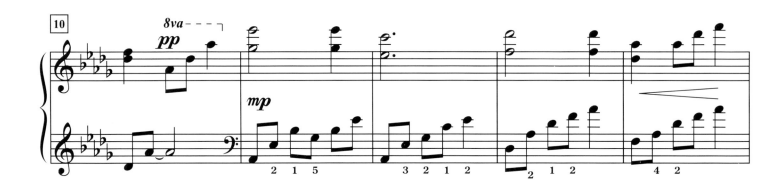

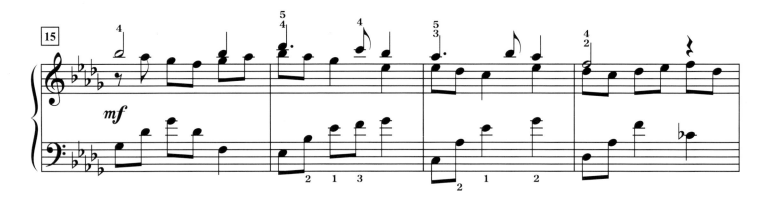

O Holy Night